COCO GOES TO AFRICA

A Story About Adoption

BY ELLA B. DELGER
AND HER GRANDMA

James & Stevie Delger

COCO GOES TO AFRICA

Dedicated to my cousin, Dagim

I was just seven when my Uncle Dave and Aunt Shanny told me they were planning to adopt a child from all the way across the world in Ethiopia. I remember wondering what it was like there, and if they ever got snow like we do where I live (they don't!) It was more than a year after Aunt Shanny and Uncle Dave told our family their good news that my cousin Dagim finally came home. It was such a long wait, but he is so worth it!

I met him for the first time at my Grandma's house. He was so adorable. I loved him right away. Our family is so fortunate we got to make Dagim a part of us. That's why Grandma and I had the idea for this book, because EVERY child deserves a story.

- Ella B.

"This is so exciting!" said Coco as he was packing his suitcase. "I can't wait to go to Africa!"

"Why are you going to Africa?" asked Coco's friend Ellie. Ellie is an elephant of course.

"We are adopting! He is a little boy and his name is Dagim. I can't wait to meet him and for him to be a part of our family," said Coco.

Coco packed his pajamas. He packed his toothbrush and toothpaste. He put his brush and his warm coat and even his flashlight into his suitcase. Then Coco zipped it up and brought it downstairs.

"I'm ready!" announced Coco. "Ready to go to Africa!"

The next day Coco got on the airplane with Mom, Dad and a whole bunch of other people he didn't even know! They flew and they flew and they flew. Sometimes Coco slept. Sometimes Coco read a book. At mealtimes, a nice lady dressed in a blue uniform gave Coco a sandwich, some chips, a cookie, and a carton of milk. It took a long time, so long that Coco wondered if they'd ever land.

And then...

The plane finally landed! They were in Africa in a country called Ethiopia. It was time to meet Dagim and take him home forever!

Coco went with his Mom and Dad to the orphanage. The windows were filled with children and Coco wondered, "Which one is Dagim? Which one could he be?"

Coco, Mom, and Dad went into a room that was called The Receiving Room. They waited for Dagim to come in.

And then...

There he was!

Dagim was a little bit scared and a little bit shy. Coco hugged him tightly and told him everything was going to be all right. "In fact," said Coco, "it's going to be wonderful! We are all one family now."

Mom, Dad, Coco, and Dagim all got on the plane together. They flew and they flew and they flew. Coco whispered to Dagim for most of the trip. Dagim was scared; he had never been on a plane before and his family was very new to him, but Coco made it better.

Coco showed Dagim their room. Coco told him that they were best friends and brothers forever. Dagim felt right at home and was so happy to finally have his very own family.